REMEM[BERING]
DAVID

CLAY BRIDGES
PRESS

DAVID O'BRIEN
ILLUSTRATED BY
DANIELLE O'BRIEN

Published by Clay Bridges Press in Houston, TX
www.ClayBridgesPress.com

Illustrations by Danielle O'Brien

ISBN 978-1-953300-62-1 (paperback)
ISBN 978-1-953300-63-8 (hardback)
ISBN 978-1-953300-64-5 (ebook)

Special Sales: Most Clay Bridges Press titles are available in special quantity discounts.
Custom imprinting or excerpting can also be done to fit special needs.
For standard bulk orders, go to www.claybridgesbulk.com.
For specialty press or large orders, contact Clay Bridges Press at info@claybridgespress.com.

DEDICATED TO MY GRANDDAUGHTER, HARPER JOY.

SPECIAL THANKS TO MY WIFE, LISA, FOR SUPPORTING ME.

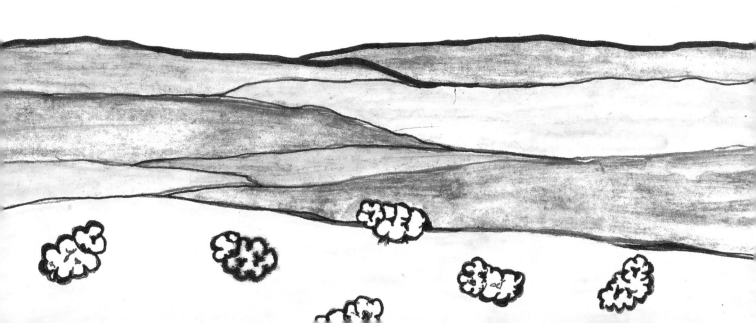

David was a little shepherd boy.

He protected the sheep

from
Lions

and
Bears.

God gave him courage.

One day David faced a giant,

Goliath.

God gave him courage.

David defeated Goliath.

When you are afraid,

remember
David.

AUTHOR
David O'Brien

ILLUSTRATOR
Danielle O'Brien

David O'Brien was born and raised in Lakeland, Florida. He gave his life to Jesus Christ at a local Baptist church there when he was seven years old. He graduated from Lake Gibson High School and then went to Virginia to work on a farm. David was searching for guidance and decided to move back to Lakeland, where he enrolled at Southeastern College and majored in elementary education. He met Lisa there, and they got married in 1987. They both graduated from college in 1989, and David began teaching at a local elementary school. They had their first son in 1989. By 2001, they had three more children. David received his Master's in reading instruction in 2007 and began teaching at the middle and high school levels. After teaching for 30 years, he retired and is now enjoying his granddaughter, Harper Joy.

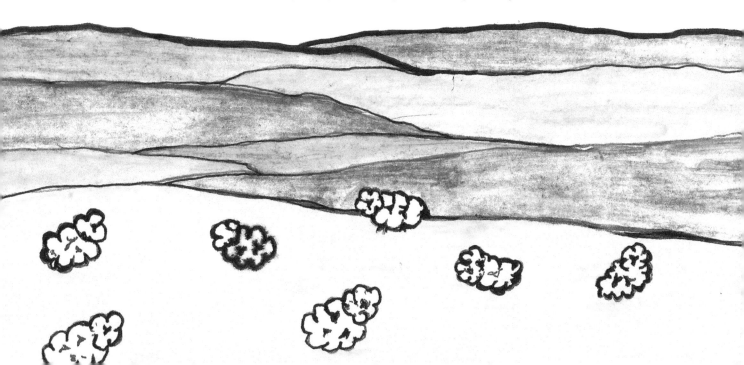

CPSIA information can be obtained
at www.ICGtesting.com
Printed in the USA
BVHW021410070921
616214BV00019B/905

9 781953 300621